Magnet Therapy

A POWERFUL HEALING FORCE

by

Rosemary Skinner SRN

I dedicate this book to my husband, Tony,
whose love, support and encouragement
have sustained me throughout our marriage.

And to my mother Kitty and my sister Kathleen,
a heartfelt thank you.

Rosemary Skinner SRN

Rosemary trained and worked as a nurse in Ireland, Britain, and Africa for over 20 years. She practiced Reflexology from 1986 after obtaining a diploma in London. In addition she has studied Health Awareness, Natural Therapy, Magnet Therapy, Aura and Chakra Balancing.

Rosemary worked with Sr. Theresa Feist, (author of *Spirituality and Holistic Living*), both in Ireland and Canada, where she studied Magnet Therapy. She has since continued her studies in America.

Rosemary facilitates workshops in Magnet Therapy, Holistic Living, Aura and Chakra Balancing and Personal Development. She has conducted workshops all over Ireland.

Rosemary runs a practice in Stillorgan, Dublin. She specialises in Magnet Therapy, Allergy Testing, Aura and Chakra Balancing.

To Joe, Marie and Eleanor without whom
none of this could possibly have happened.
I will always be indebted.

A warm thank you to Bridie, Josephine and Sara
for all the encouragement.

Foreword

This book was written as a result of many requests from therapists and friends working in the area of Complementary Medicine.

I have drawn as much information as possible from my ten years experience in the study, theory and practice of Magnet Therapy.

The first section of the book deals with the background and history of Magnet Therapy. The next section is an overview of magnetism and an explanation of the different types of magnets. The final section details the use of Magnet Therapy in the treatment of various conditions.

The most recent research and scientific information available world-wide points the way to a very positive future for the role of Magnet Therapy in both fields of Medicine and Complementary Medicine.

I hope this book will serve as not only a text book on the subject, but also as an inspiration to others to explore this exciting field of Complementary Medicine.

CONTENTS

Preface

Magnet Therapy is a natural, simple, non-invasive treatment.

The principle involves the use of magnets to generate magnetic fields which are used to regulate pathogenic disorders present in the body cells and structures.

It is used by today's practitioners to stimulate the body's self-healing process.

It has also been used successfully in treating various wide ranging conditions, for example:
Pain control & relief
Colds & flu
Sore throat
Stress
Arthritis
Broken bones and sprains
Some heart conditions

In all cases Magnet Therapy has been shown to achieve remarkable results in the alleviation of pain.

What is Magnetism?

Magnetism is one of the strongest forces in the universe.

It is a fundamental force of nature produced by the motion of charged particles such as electrons, indicating the close relationship between magnetism and electricity. The most familiar evidence of magnetism is the attractive or repulsive force observed to act between magnetic materials such as iron.

HOW DOES IT WORK?

Because a magnetic field improves blood circulation in living tissue, it is an excellent way of treating all forms of pain.

It controls the rotation of the earth and all the other planets in our universe. Our bodies survive on our own magnetism.

As an example of specific effects created when a magnetic field is applied to the body, below are typical changes that have been documented:

1. Electricity is generated in blood vessels.

2. Ionised particles increase in the blood.

3. Autonomic nerves are excited.

4. Circulation is improved.

Many years of research and clinical application have shown that the simple introduction of a magnetic field can provide stimulation and enhancement of the lymphatic system as well as every cell within the body.

The magnetic field does not heal; it merely aids the cells in creating an optimum environment in which the body can begin to heal itself. Between the circulatory, lymphatic and neurological effects, outstanding advances in health can be obtained.

Variations in the earth's magnetic field are important to all living beings on the planet. Scientists are aware that this field is in constant flux as it is influenced by solar winds, shifts in the earth's core and the presence of ferromagnetic substances in the earth's crust.

Current research shows that the earth's field periodically waxes and wanes and even reverses itself entirely. Though the reasons for this are not known, geological evidence indicates that the strength of the field gradually grows weaker, reaches minimum levels or disappears entirely and then builds in the opposite direction, resulting in a reversal of the North and South magnetic poles. Scientists estimate that such reversals occur about every one-half to one million years. The most recent reversal took place about 700,000 years ago.

Other scientists have documented that the earth's magnetic field has degraded about 50% over the last 500-1,000 years, with a 5% decline being recorded in the past 100 years. Calculations are that if this degradation continues at its present rate, there will not be a sufficient magnetic field to support life within 1,500 years.

Interestingly, certain locations on earth have inexplicably retained the strength of their magnetic fields. For example, areas near Sedona, Arizona, USA and Lourdes, France are destinations to which countless people travel annually to experience feelings of well being and to seek healing.

Much current research is directed toward the electrical nature of life. Scientists have established beyond any doubt that all living cells are electrical in nature. The functioning of the cells and nervous system of every living being is based on direct current (DC) and pulsed energy (AC). Without this energy, there is no life. Each individual cell possesses a positive electrical charge at its nucleus and a negative electrical charge on its outer membrane.

The History of Magnet Therapy

Today, there is a re-awakening in the use of magnetism in the field of therapeutics. Through innovative design and revolutionary applications, biomagnetism is finding an ever-increasing niche in the health care fields of many countries throughout the world. To fully understand this phenomenon and the potential it has in our world today, it is helpful to look at some historical applications and factors about magnetism.

HOW LONG HAVE MAGNETS BEEN AROUND?

Nature itself manufactured the first magnet ever - lodestone - a mixture of lava rock, iron and minerals. Molten lava spewed from erupting volcanoes, cooled and hardened and due to its iron content, retained the earth's magnetism. With the passage of time, lava eventually broke up into small rocks - natural magnets.

Early man soon discovered that the lodestone was attracted to other stones that contained iron.

The ancient Egyptians discovered a great deal about magnetism and utilised its energy and power in pyramid design and construction.

For thousands of years, mankind has utilised the beneficial powers of magnetism knowing little about the specific reasons why it worked or the effects it created, but realising only that curative results could be achieved.

The oldest known usage of magnetic powers is traced to Africa where an African bloodstone (magnetite) more than 100,000 years old, has been found. The magnetite was ground up and used in potions, foods and topical applications.

In Ancient Greece, Aristotle was the first person in recorded history to speak of the therapeutic properties of the natural magnets of his time and indeed, most of the ancient civilisations, including the Hebrews, Arabs, Indians, Egyptians and Chinese used magnets for healing.

It is recorded that around 2000 BC the Greek physician, Galen, found that pain from many different types of illness could be relieved by applying natural magnets.

In the First Century, the Chinese began documenting effects on health and disease related to variations in the earth's magnetic field, using very sensitive compasses to monitor those variations. Around 1000 AD a Persian physician documented the use of magnets to relieve disorders such as gout and muscle spasms.

Later records show magnets were used for strengthening muscles and bones, smoothing joint articulation, nourishing the kidneys and even improving impaired eyesight.

The first in-depth study of the history of magnetic treatment of diseases was undertaken in 1777 by France's Royal Society of Medicine. Additional studies included reports by Eydam in 1843, Charot and Renard in 1878, Westphal and Gangee in 1878, Mueller in 1879, Benedict and Drozdoz in 1879, Benedict in 1885 and Quinan in 1886.

Franz Mesmer (1734-1815) successfully used magnets for the treatment of many diseases in Vienna. He wrote a book about the theory of animal magnetism which is considered to be the foundation for modern Hypnosis and Suggestive Therapy, hence the expression "mesmerised".

Magnet Therapy and Modern Science

For the past twenty years or so much of the focus has been placed on Biochemistry for the answers in medicine. Biophysics has been neglected but now appears to be on the verge of making an equally valuable contribution.

Twenty years ago, Dr Raymond Damadian wrote a pioneering paper on Nuclear Magnetic Resonance (MRI) and how it could be used in the detection of cancer. The initial paper was visionary and far ahead of its time. Dr Damadian received the National Medal of Technology from President Reagan on 5 July 1988 for his discovery of the MRI machine.

Recent discoveries in the fields of Biomagnetics has led to the addition of new diagnostic tools. Other instruments include the SQUID - Superconducting Quantum Interface Detector for determining minute magnetic fields including those in living organisms; Magnetoencephalogram - an improvement over the Electroencephalogram EEG machine; Xomed Magnetic Hearing Aid and many other devices. The research is ongoing.

Dr William Philpott MD and author of *Brain Allergies - The Psychonutrient Connection* gave up using electric shock treatment some years ago. He recommends using negative - North Pole state magnetic fields that are considerably safer and that have proved effective through the years, on thousands of his own patients. Natural solid state magnets do not create shock, rather balance the brain's energy field without electric current and at low fields intensity, which is more receptive to the human system.

Many conditions are immediately relieved.

Doctors in both Europe and the United States are obtaining results using electromagnetic fields to treat damage ranging from ulcers to severe burns. Soft tissue injuries are responding well as are those of bone and joint. In the Soviet Union, doctors regularly use magnets to speed wound healing after surgery, to improve circulation and to strengthen and mend bones.

An American dentist, Dr Jack Prince, has successfully used magnets on acupuncture points to reduce bleeding, gagging and pain sensitivity. Dr Prince found that magnets could bring immediate relief of chronic pain from jaw dislocations as well as from TMJ syndrome, headaches and teeth grinding.

Another effect of a magnetic field that is well documented and supported by the laws of physics is the enhancement of blood circulation and lymphatic drainage.

The Japanese have mainly concentrated research on the effect of magnets on stiff shoulders, hypertension, fatigue and constipation.

The Russians experimented with magnetised water which dissolves kidney and gall bladder stones.

In England researchers found a simple method of separating red blood vessels from blood plasma and other blood cells using magnets, a technique which has considerable medical implications.

As blood cells contain about 4% iron they show great affinity towards magnets. In the USA, Dr Albert Roy Davis carried out experiments on mice which have greatly helped in the vital stages of the development of the use of magnets in the treatment of cancer.

For example, when mice were injected with cancer cells the application of the North Pole of the magnet to the cancer cells brought about a reduction in the size of the cancer cells and eventually the cancer cells died.

Albert Roy Davis and many others including the Indian physicians Doctors Bansal and Bansal have stated that cancer cannot exist in a strong magnetic field. Doctors from the USA, Portugal and Japan have been successful in the treatment of cancer patients with Magnet Therapy.

The most recent development in this field was the discovery of the universal Cancer Spiral Theory by Professor Wollin a Swedish scientist.

In 1983 the Super Magnet was developed by Sumittomo in Japan for Professor Wollin.

Kyoichi Nakagawa MD, one of the world's foremost authorities on magnetism and its therapeutic effects on the human body, claims that the continuing degrading of the earth's magnetic field, combined with man's electronic environment, is responsible for a broad range of ailments which he labels as the Magnetic Deficiency Syndrome. These ailments include stiffness of the shoulders, back and neck, low back pain, chest pains for no specific reason, habitual headaches and heaviness of the head, dizziness and insomnia for uncertain reasons, habitual constipation and general fatigue.

Types of Magnets used in Magnet Therapy

Man-made magnets have strong magnetic fields and can be of differing shapes, sizes and power and hence can be utilised for healing purposes. Man-made magnets can be made into permanent or temporary magnets.

Permanent magnets retain their magnetism for a long time. Temporary magnets can be switched on and off at will and are called electromagnets. These magnets exist only as long as electricity is passing through them.

Today, a variety of man-made magnets are available - Neodymium (Super Magnet), Ceramic, and Iron - in a wide range of sizes and strengths.

Artificial magnets are made by winding an insulated coil around a bar of magnetic material and passing a direct electrical current through the coil with the help of an electric cell.

COMPOSITION

Modern permanent magnets are made up of an alloy of aluminium, nickel, iron and cobalt in various proportions depending on the power required.

SUPER MAGNET

An exceptionally powerful magnet having the addition of Neodymium, a rare earth metal, hence the differing costs depending on the strength of the magnet to a large degree.

CERAMIC MAGNETS

Some magnets are made from synthetic material and are referred to as ceramic magnets. These magnets are liable to break on being dropped.

STRONG MAGNETS

Magnets are available in high strengths, and are referred to as Strong Magnets.

MAGNETIC BEDS

A Magnetic Bed is usually a specially designed mattress with magnets distributed throughout. It is possible to make your own magnetic mattress, using small ferrite magnets North side up 3 to 4 inches apart.

MEASUREMENT OF STRENGTH

The strength of a magnet or its magnetic field is measured by an instrument called a Gaussmeter. A typical strength of a small bar magnet might be 2,600 gauss. As these instruments are generally only available in laboratories, strength is commonly measured in terms of the iron weight it can lift, the Super Magnet being the strongest.

NB. Horseshoe or household magnets are not suitable for healing.

There are two types of magnets used in Magnet Therapy, UNIPOLE and BIPOLAR Magnets.

1. Unipole magnets are polarised with negative energy on one side and positive energy on the opposite side.

2. When both positive and negative energy is present on the same side of a magnet, the magnet is referred to as Bipolar.

When a weak magnet is exposed to a strong unipole magnet the polarity of the weak magnet is over-ridden and the weak magnet assumes the polarity of the exposure from the stronger magnet during that period. When the weak magnet is separated from the strong unipole magnet it returns to being a single magnet with two poles of equal strength.

Know Your Magnet

POLARISATION

All magnets have two poles - North Pole and South Pole. Electrons (magnetic energy) from the North Pole spin left (counterclockwise) generating negative magnetic energy while electrons from the South Pole spin right (clockwise) generating positive magnetic energy. This discovery has been reported and confirmed by sophisticated space-age instruments which measure magnetic energy.

Both poles of a magnet differ in nature and possess different therapeutic properties, therefore, the marking of poles is of basic importance for Magnet Therapy. Another aspect of magnetism is that opposite poles attract each other, but like poles repel each other.

The Law of Polarity: Opposite forces attract while like forces repel.

Negative magnetic energy will be referred to as North Pole and positive magnetic energy will be referred to as South Pole. The terminology "negative" and "positive" has no reference to "good" and "bad" but rather relates to the laws of electricity and physics.

DIFFERENCES IN POLARITY IDENTIFICATION

In purchasing magnets, the reader must be aware and cautioned that the poles of magnets are identified by two opposite systems:

1. Traditional method of identification used in industry and navigation (opposite of the earth's polarity).

2. Physics identification of the magnetic Poles corresponding with the earth's magnetic poles.

Biophysics recognises and equates cellular and tissue polarity with the earth's magnetic poles.

NB. Another caution. Some authors (especially foreign authors and medical practitioners) have continued to use the traditional industrial method of identifying polarities. It is, therefore, of utmost importance that before getting involved in biomagnetics, the reader understands the Law of Polarity and establishes the true identity of the poles (corresponding to earth's poles) of the magnets to be used.

HOW TO IDENTIFY THE POLE OF A MAGNET

While it is important to use the proper pole of the magnet, not all manufacturers identify the poles on their magnets and some identify them differently depending on which method used - industrial or physics identification. Here is a way to solve the problem.

You will need a compass for this exercise. (See diagram opposite.)

First establish the North/South axis using the compass.
Hold magnet next to the compass. When the compass needle (which is North seeking) marked N points to the magnet it indicates the North (negative) Pole side of the magnet. (Opposites attract.)

I always identify the poles of magnets and then label using a red sticker to indicate the South Pole and a blue sticker to indicate the North Pole.

NORTH POLE OF MAGNET
(Label with blue sticker)

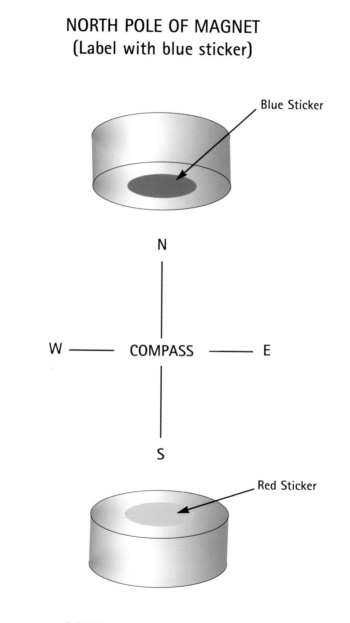

Blue Sticker

N

W ——— COMPASS ——— E

S

Red Sticker

SOUTH POLE OF MAGNET
(Label with red sticker)

Magnet Therapy - Side Effects and Precautions

SIDE EFFECTS

Generally speaking side effects are minimal.

Initially a person may feel light headed (dizzy), nauseous or tired. Some people experience difficulty until they get used to the magnetic field. The symptoms are usually more marked in women rather than men.

If such discomfort is experienced, the magnet or magnets should be removed and re-introduced at a later stage and for a shorter period of time initially, to allow the body to adapt to the magnetic field.

If pain does increase following application of magnets, the position of the magnets may be changed but not necessarily removed.

People on medication may find that their dosage needs to be adjusted so it is important that they keep in contact with their doctor.

PRECAUTIONS

Magnet Therapy is not suitable under the following conditions:

1. During pregnancy.

2. Bypass surgery as there are staples in the chest.

3. People with pacemakers as magnets can affect the batteries.

4. People with artificial joints because of metal pins or plates.

- Magnetic beds should not be used if a person has any of the above conditions. Do not use Magnetic beds for 24 hours daily if ill. The adrenal function could be suppressed with slow energy recovery.

- Do not put your magnet near credit cards because it could render them inoperable.

- Do not put your magnet near tapes, videos or computers as they may become damaged.

- Do not place your magnet on top of television sets as it can affect the tubes.

General Application of Magnets

Magnet Therapy treatments are carried out in two ways:

1. LOCAL
   Local treatment is the application of North Pole to the site of
   pain and inflammation.

2. GENERAL
   General treatment is for wellbeing or when the illness affects
   the whole body e.g. arthritis.

The Super Magnet can be worn on the thymus gland, North Pole
placed on the body over the gland.

Ceramic Magnets - North and South Pole can be applied to the
palms of hands and soles of feet. For upper body problems, place
under the palms of the hands, for lower body place under the soles
of the feet.

North Pole is applied to the right side of the body and South Pole is
applied to the left side of the body, palms of hands or soles of feet-
North Pole under right and South Pole under left.

If magnets are applied to the upper and lower parts of the body, the
North Pole should be applied to the upper body and the South Pole
to the lower part of the body.

When the front and back of the body are being treated, the North Pole should be applied to the front of the body and South Pole to the back of the body.

It should be noted that the application of magnets depends on the condition being treated.

POSITION OF SUPER MAGNET

The Super Magnet can be held in position by placing the magnet against the skin under your undergarments and by placing a steel washer or similar magnetic attracting material on the outside of the garment. Certain coins can be used as an alternative to the steel washer - Canadian Dollar coin, Euro 5 cent, Sterling 2 pence (post 1990)

Magnetised Water

Drinking magnetically treated water is very effective as a preventative treatment and is of therapeutic value. A minimum of two to three 8 fl oz glasses can be taken daily before meals.

NORTH POLE

North Pole magnetised water is good for external complaints i.e. wounds, swollen eyes, spots and eye infections. In the case of swollen eyes or eye infections bathe eyes with North Pole magnetised water.

North Pole water is always used for infections and influenzas.

North Pole water aids the digestion and regulates bowel movement. It is wonderful for infections and any kind of internal disharmony. North Pole magnetised water has a very calming effect on the system. It also helps clear urates out of the kidneys.

SOUTH POLE

South Pole magnetised water is more beneficial when the various organs of the body become sluggish e.g. the digestive system. South Pole water tones the internal muscles and improves peristalsis. Hence, in certain conditions like, dysuria (painful urination), dullness of the mind and low blood pressure the use of the South Pole magnet is invaluable.

Also for elderly people who feel weak or chilly all the time, the South Pole magnetised water improves circulation and gives a feeling of comfort and warmth and also aids digestion.

BIPOLAR
(mixed water)

Bipolar water is used to treat headaches, loss of appetite, nerve pain and muscular atrophy. It can also be used in conditions like cervical spondylitis, rheumatoid arthritis, sciatica and gout.

A glass of Bipolar magnetised water can be taken in the morning as an energy booster or, if a person is fatigued after a day's work, an additional glass can be taken in the evening.

Bipolar water is also beneficial for non-specific complaints.

TO MAGNETISE WATER

To magnetise water, stand a glass or bottle of water on the North or South pole of magnet depending on the type of water required.

The stronger the force of the magnet the quicker water is magnetised. The strong Super Magnet will magnetise water in five to ten minutes. Because of their lower power, Ceramic Magents take twelve hours to magnetise.

To make Bipolar magnetised water you need two magnets and two glasses or bottles of water. Stand one 8 fl oz glass or bottle on the North Pole of the magnet and the other on the South Pole of the second magnet for twelve hours if using Ceramic Magnets and five to ten minutes if using Super Magnets.

After the appropriate length of time the waters are removed and can be mixed or else kept separately and mixed as required.

STORAGE

Magnetised water should be covered and used within five days.

MILK

To magnetise milk stand an 8 fl oz glass of milk on the South Pole of a Super Magnet for twenty minutes.

This is an effective treatment for children and adults who have a sensitivity to milk.

OILS

Oils can also be magnetised. Oils must be kept on the magnets for a much longer time - two weeks if possible. As oils are thicker in density they take a longer time to magnetise. It is also advisable to stir the oil every day or alternate days so that the effect of magnetism reaches the entire fluid.

How Long Does Magnet Therapy Take To Produce Results?

This is one of the questions frequently asked.

In some very painful conditions people may experience instant relief.

Magnet Therapy treatment is not a miraculous cure. You cannot expect to begin treatment in the morning and be healed by the end of the day. If the illness is acute it will probably respond much quicker, but if the condition has become chronic it will obviously take longer and sometimes the improvement may be so gradual that it is hardly noticeable.

Whatever the duration of the recovery, it is important to continue your routine treatment using magnetic placement.

Good Health – A Balance of Energy
Good health is a balance of positive and negative energy.

During the day the positive magnetic energy drive of physical activity and mental concentration is higher than the negative magnetic energy. During the night the negative magnetic energy drive is higher than the positive magnetic energy drive in the body. When we wake from a good night's sleep, the positive and negative magnetic energies are equal, leading to a state of balance.

Today, however, with the erosion of the earth's magnetic field, the high stress of modern day living and general decline in proper nutrition can lead to a weakened immune system and in some cases food allergies and addictions including chemical toxins. A further environmental health threat seems to be the electromagnetic radiation from power lines, computer terminals and household appliances.

An imbalance arises when positive magnetic energy strength exceeds negative magnetic energy strength for very long periods of time causing physical or emotional symptoms to occur.

Many of the disorders and diseases caused today are said to be the result of electromagnetic breakdown. When a magnetic or oxygen deficiency occurs in an organ or system, symptoms of illness arise and normal cell division is adversely affected. A growing number of doctors and researchers believe that the application of North Pole magnetic energy causes oxygenation of tissues by creating a field of high energy with an increased number of electrons.

Dr William H Philpott, whose research and works I have studied in depth, has successfully used Magnet Therapy on thousands of patients over the past decade. He, among a variety of researchers and practitioners, believes that negative magnetic energy is the primary healer and induces melatonin production which is anti-ageing, anti-stress and controls free radicals that cause many of our known diseases.

This positive/negative polarisation allows each cell to function in an orderly and healthy manner. As cells perform their normal functions, this electromagnetic charge wears down. The body attempts to revitalise these "tired" cells by sending pulses of electromagnetic energy from the brain through the nervous system to recharge the cells and strengthen the polarised field.

This energy can be diminished or blocked by conditions found throughout today's environment, resulting in a host of modern maladies. These range from headaches and fatigue to tumours and disruption of both circulatory and digestive systems, along with other specific and non-specific ailments.

The earth produces its own DC magnetic pulses that support the natural biorhythms of all living things. However, as mentioned previously, scientists are becoming increasingly alarmed that the present-day magnetic field of the earth has diminished significantly and continues to do so.

Stress and How it Affects Us

Stress plays a very big part in breaking down the defence mechanisms in the body. However, some stress is necessary. There are situations in our lives when it is essential that our bodies cope with the demands made on them. Every illness has an emotional base. We are all unique; each one of us has our characteristic psychological make up. That is why in similar situations we react differently, our reactions being the product of our individual traits.

The real purpose of our lives is not complete freedom from pain and suffering, but our ability to accept pain without resentment and to face it with courage. Pain and suffering are integral parts of who we are. Life becomes more meaningful when we meet these challenges. It is not important whether we win or lose.

Can we really appreciate good health if we have not suffered illness? It is the experience of pain and suffering that makes good things in life more sweet. The difficulties of life do not weigh us down so much as our resistance to accepting and facing them. Resistance to the unfavourable conditions around us is the root cause of emotional stress. By facing and accepting these conditions especially when they are unavoidable, a further undue stress is avoided. How often in our own lives are we faced with unpleasant decisions and we do everything in our power to avoid making such a decision. We run around the place seeking advice and more advice, heeding possibly none of it and at the same time heightening our own stress to an unacceptable level. Eventually, when all the running is over and there is nothing left to do but make the decision, we suddenly cannot believe the relief that comes with making such a decision.

Undue stress can cloud the thinking process and make it more difficult to deal with the complex problems facing us. This can lead to problems being blown out of all proportion. By accepting what cannot be changed the mind will remain reasonably calm and be in a better condition to deal with difficult issues.

When emotions are suppressed the stress factor increases considerably. Such emotions as anger, grief, resentment and many others if not dealt with in an appropriate manner will eventually express themselves in the form of illness. Crying is a wonderful expression of pent up emotions and it keeps the stress levels down.

Of all the negative feelings that disturb our emotional and physiological states, the greatest one is fear. Our greatest fear becomes our biggest nightmare. So many of us are made miserable with irrational fear of the future or are tormented by mistakes of the past. We must remember the past is gone, the future is unknown. If we have learned from our past mistakes that is the greatest testimony of who we are. To live in the now is all there is, to savour each moment. One of the greatest gifts we all have within us is an ability to forgive ourselves for our past mistakes and to be able to love and support ourselves in the process that is the true essence of who we are.

Pain and Disease

Pain and disease begin when conditions cause the capillary pores to dilate and allow the escape of significant quantities of blood proteins into the cellular area. This crowding of the proteins attracts fluid (inflammation), causes pain and deprives some of the cells in the area of proper oxygen and nutrients, resulting in poor cellular functioning. These malfunctioning cells, if not carried away and disposed of by the lymphatic system, begin to destroy healthy cells.

According to Dr C Samuel West, chemist and internationally recognised lymphologist, trapped blood proteins are the one common denominator present in all pain and disease. His many years of research have shown that trapped blood proteins, on a moderate scale, produce the conditions on a cellular level that cause pain, inflammation, viral infections, bacterial infections, allergies, parasites, low energy levels, heart disease, cancer, obesity, high blood pressure, arthritis, multiple sclerosis, polio, cerebral palsy and all the other crippling and serious diseases known to man.

Since pain can be caused by different conditions the cause of the pain should be determined.

Because a magnetic field improves circulation in living tissue, it is an excellent way of treating all forms of pain. Pain is a signal from the nervous system that something is wrong. In most cases the nerves are stimulated chemically. With lumbago or back pain a vertebra has shifted position causing the tissue to tighten and so mechanically trigger cramps in the affected areas which means that waste products such as lactic acid are prevented from escaping thus irritating the nerves.

Treatment with Magnetic Therapy improves circulation so that waste products are removed and the pain diminishes.

Pain can also be caused by a pressure from fluid build up within a joint or other encapsulated area. Since North Pole energy pulls additional fluid into the treated area, pain can increase if direct application is made to a joint already full of fluid. In this instance moving the magnet above, below or to the side will pull fluid from the affected area and may relieve pain.

Pain may also be caused by inflammation of a joint or other area. In this instance direct application of the North Pole of the magnet provides relief by reducing swelling and inflammation. For localised pain, application of the North Pole of the magnet over the area of pain will give quick relief. Treatment can be continued until symptoms are relieved.

For general chronic pain a magnetic bed which provides full body therapy is beneficial.

Healing with Magnet Therapy

Circulatory System

BLOOD PRESSURE

(Blood pressure is the force or pressure which the blood exerts on the walls of the vessels in which it is contained.)

NB. A person suffering from a blood pressure complaint needs to see their physician. Magnet Therapy is a wonderful complement to orthodox medicine.

HYPERTENSION

(High Blood Pressure.)

Hypertension is diagnosed when the resting blood pressure (diastolic) is persistently raised. There are usually no symptoms felt. If left untreated it increases risk of strokes and other disorders. A continuous elevation in blood pressure is the pressure which blood exerts within the blood vessels. Since the heart is a pump it alternates between contractions and relaxation. The contraction phase is called systolic and the relaxation phase is known as diastolic. Blood pressure is commonly measured as two numbers. The systolic pressure refers to the pressure of the heart at work and the lower diastolic number is the pressure of the heart relaxing. The diastolic pressure is the more important one it tells how much rest your heart is getting.

High blood pressure is due primarily to a spasm of the muscles of the arteries but it can be brought on by atheroclerosis.

Treatment

A magnetic bed used in conjunction with a magnetic pillow is recommended. The kidneys should be treated daily with North Pole and South Pole magnets.

North Pole right kidney, South Pole left kidney ten to fifteen minutes daily.

Application of the North Pole of the Super Magnet to the crown of the head overnight.

Also place North Pole of the magnet to the occipital area of head (back of head/base of skull) morning and evening for ten to fifteen minutes.

HYPOTENSION
(Low Blood Pressure.)

Some people have normally low blood pressure and it becomes a problem when the blood pressure has fallen to the extent that the blood flow to the brain is reduced causing dizziness and fainting. Symptoms can occur while standing or sitting.

Treatment

The North Pole of the magnet should be applied to adrenal glands and 7th cervical vertebrae (back of neck) for ten to fifteen minutes morning and evening. May be used more frequently initially until symptoms are relieved.

HEART CONDITIONS

The heart is basically a hollow muscular organ. It is divided into four chambers and is covered by two layers of pericardium.

Treatment

The North Pole of a magnet is effective in normalising cardiac irregularities such as palpitations and tachycardia and also helps strengthen the heart.

NB. Please note that the South Pole is never used over the heart area as it can cause tachycardia (an increase of the heart rate above normal).

IMPORTANT: Do not use any magnets if a person has a pacemaker or had bypass surgery.

Place the North Pole and South Pole under hands and feet for ten minutes morning and evening - North Pole right foot and hand, South Pole left foot and hand.

Take 4 fl ozs South Pole magnetised water twice daily.

RAISED CHOLESTEROL

(An unacceptable level of fat like material present in the blood.)

Treatment

Place the North Pole of the magnet under right foot and South Pole under left foot for twenty minutes twice daily.

Take 6 fl ozs Bipolar magnetised water twice daily.

GOUT

(Metabolic condition which affects various joints of the body due to excessive deposits of uric acid in the tissues.)

Gout usually affects small joints like toes and fingers. The causes are usually attributed to high living and a diet rich in protein. The affected joints are usually red in colour, hot and painful.

Treatment

The application of the North Pole of the magnet should be applied locally to the toes or affected area.

If the toe or affected area is extremely painful to the touch then use the small Super Magnet as its weight will not be nearly as heavy.

Take 4 fl ozs Bipolar magnetised water four times daily.

It should be noted that a simple balanced diet with a minimum amount of protein, plus physical exercise are absolutely necessary.

VARICOSE VEINS
Treatment

Use magnetic insoles in the shoes daily.

Also magnets can be placed under soles of feet morning and evening for ten to twenty minutes, North Pole - right foot, South Pole - left foot.

This treatment is also very beneficial for people with poor circulation.

Digestive System

Digestive problems can be created by food allergies. If an allergy is suspected allergy testing is recommended.

NB. It is important not to carry out treatment after a meal in order to allow peristaltic action to take place.

North Pole of the magnet under palm of right hand and South Pole under left foot for twenty minutes twice daily has a beneficial effect on the digestive system.

DYSPEPSIA

(Indigestion or difficult digestion is termed as dyspepsia.)

It is usually experienced in the form of discomfort or pain in the stomach, heartburn or flatulence. There may be many causes of this condition for example, overeating and over indulgence in certain substances particularly pastries.

Treatment

The North Pole of a magnet can be applied to the area of the stomach, liver and colon.

Also apply magnets under hands and feet morning and evening - North Pole under right hand and right foot, South Pole under left hand and left foot for twenty minutes twice daily.

Bipolar magnetised water is very effective for chronic dyspepsia. Take 4 fl ozs every two hours for acute attacks and four times daily for chronic cases.

It is important to chew food slowly and well.

FLATULENCE
(Wind.)

Flatulence is an accumulation of gas in the stomach and in the intestine and is a common symptom of dyspepsia.

The flatulence causes bloating, discomfort and sometimes pain. Some of the causes are defective digestion and intake of excessively starchy food which escapes digestion in the small intestine and ferments in the large intestine due to the action of intestinal bacteria.

Treatment

Magnets can be applied under the soles of the feet morning and evening for twenty minutes - North Pole under the right foot and South Pole under the left foot.

Additional placement of the North Pole of the magnet over the colon can give relief.

The North Pole of a strong magnet over the colon at night is beneficial.

Take 6 fl ozs Bipolar magnetised water morning and evening.

COLITIS
(Inflammation of the wall of the colon.)

Treatment

The North Pole of the magnet applied to the abdominal area to include the liver, gall bladder and colon for fifteen minutes twice daily. The North Pole of the magnet can be worn over the colon at night.

Take 6 fl ozs North Pole magnetised water three times daily before meals.

CROHN'S DISEASE
(Condition in which segments of the alimentary tract become inflamed, thickened and ulcerated.)

Treatment

The North Pole of a Ceramic Magnet applied to the abdominal area for thirty minutes twice daily.

Take 6 fl ozs North Pole magnetised water three times daily before meals.

If the disease is acute, magnetised water can be taken up to five times daily.

DIVERTICULITIS
(Inflammation of the divericulum which is caused by infection.)

Treatment

For pain and discomfort place the North Pole of the magnet directly over the colon area for ten to fifteen minutes twice daily.

Also treat liver and gall bladder until symptoms are relieved. Magnetic strip can also be used if necessary.

Take 6 fl ozs North Pole magnetised water twice daily.

IRRITABLE BOWEL SYNDROME
(Spastic Colon.)

A common condition in which there is recurrent abdominal pain with constipation and/or diarrhoea. May continue for years without any deterioration in health.

Treatment

Apply the North Pole of the magnet over abdominal area. Duration of time depends on how quickly symptoms are relieved.

Take 6 fl ozs North Pole magnetised water twice daily.

CONSTIPATION
Treatment

The North Pole of the magnet is worn over the abdomen at night.

North Pole energy pulls fluid into the colon, softening the stool and allowing natural elimination to take place. It is also a good idea to treat the liver and gall bladder area with the North Pole of the magnet for fifteen minutes twice daily.

Take 6 fl ozs North Pole magnetised water two to three times daily.

CANDIDA ALBICANS

In our intestinal tract are minute organisms called intestinal flora which are bacteria responsible for the absorption of nutrients and elimination of waste products. So we have friendly and unfriendly bacteria in the gut. This does not cause a problem as long as there is a balance between the two.

Unfortunately, with modern living and deficiencies in the immune system, the unfriendly bacteria called candida can get out of hand and causes a great deal of problems. The overgrowth is caused by what we eat, chlorine in the water, increased use of antibiotics, the contraceptive pill, mercury fillings and the introduction of antibiotics and hormones in meat.

If the immune system is weakened the candida spreads rapidly. The symptoms vary and may include bloating, indigestion, flatulence, cystitis, thrush, fungal infections, constipation, bad breath, recurring sore throats, mood swings, headaches, anxiety, depression, tiredness, dizziness - the list is endless.

Candida grows in an acidic environment within the intestinal tract. In a healthy body the cell is slightly alkaline.

Treatment
Place the North Pole of the magnet over colon nightly.

Take 6 fl ozs North Pole magnetised water twice daily.

A reduction in refined sugars and yeast is necessary.

It is of vital importance that the appropriate diet is adhered to.

GALL BLADDER
(Gall Stones, Blockages in the Gall Bladder.)

Treatment
Place the North Pole of strong magnet over the gall bladder for thirty minutes, twice daily until symptoms subside.

In acute cases strap the North Pole of Super Magnet overnight on gall bladder area.

Take 6 fl ozs North Pole magnetised water three times daily.

Contact doctor if symptoms do not subside.

LIVER

The liver is the largest internal organ in the body. As well as many other important functions it is an important site of metabolism of carbohydrates, proteins and fats. It is the main powerhouse of the body. Vitamins A, B12, D and K are stored in the liver.

HYPOGLYCAEMIA
(Low Blood Sugar.)

We need sugar to fuel and energise our bodies. Unfortunately in this age of instant everything we go for the quick fix of refined sugars like sweets, biscuits and chocolate instead of eating sugar in its natural form of fruit and sugar cane. These refined sugars have been over-processed and are too readily absorbed by the body. This causes a rush of sugar into the blood stream. An excess of blood sugar in the blood stream is dangerous. The pancreas is forced to produce insulin to remove the excess and in doing so our bodies are deprived of the necessary nutrients and the pancreas is over-worked. This can cause cravings, mood swings and leaves us physically, mentally and emotionally drained. Unfortunately, the liver can become very toxic which will affect the blood sugar levels.

If we eat sugars in the form of complex carbohydrate food i.e. rice, wheat, root vegetables and fruit then the foods are slowly broken down in the body into glucose which is steadily released into the blood stream giving us sustained energy. If the intake of glucose exceeds the requirements of the body the excess is converted with glycogen and stored by the liver until needed.

Treatment

Application of the North Pole of a magnet to the liver area twice daily - starting with ten to fifteen minutes, working up to thirty minutes depending on condition.

Take 4 fl ozs North Pole magnetised water three times daily before meals.

HAEMORRHOIDS
(Piles.)

Treatment

For best results sit on the North Pole of a Ceramic Magnet for twenty minutes morning and evening.

Take 6 fl ozs Bipolar water twice daily.

MOUTH PROBLEMS

Gum boils, abscesses, infection, pyorrhoea are responsible for various disorders of the gums.

Treatment

The North Pole of a magnet placed against the affected area will relieve the pain and inflammation and will arrest the growth and multiplication of bacteria.

Gargle regularly with North Pole magnetised water. Boil and cool water before magnetising

It is beneficial to add a little salt to the magnetised water. Also a diet rich in Vitamin C should be taken, if not, a Vitamin C supplement should be taken regularly.

NB. Do not treat if there are any metals in the mouth as the magnet may adhere itself to braces

Endocrine System

THYMUS GLAND

The thymus gland is situated behind the upper sternum. In relation to body size the thymus is at its largest at birth. It doubles in size by puberty after which it gradually shrinks and up to recent times it was thought that it became less effective at this stage. Now science has discovered that the thymus gland is an important controller of life. Our immunity depends on the production of the hormone thymosin which is produced by the thymus necessary for the production of T Cells (white blood cells). Our bodies cannot produce T Cells if the thymus is not working. T Cells are a necessary part of the body's immune response to sudden trauma, accidents etc.

In the case of a person who develops recurring infections it is caused by the fact that the thymus is not producing enough T Cells and therefore, cannot fight infection.

It is difficult to stimulate the thymus gland but one way of stimulating it is to lightly bang the chest rapidly and rhythmically.

Treatment

The North Pole of a magnet worn on thymus gland for one to two hours daily.

Take 4 fl ozs glass of Bipolar water three times daily.

THYROID GLAND
HYPOTHYROIDISM

(Under-activity of the thyroid gland and therefore, an under-production of thyroid hormone which stimulates energy.)

Classic symptoms are general tiredness, lethargy, constipation, weight gain and spasm. An underactive thyroid gland is diagnosed by blood test and the standard treatment is thyroxin tablets. Blood tests are taken at regular intervals and thyroxin tablets adjusted as necessary.

Hypothyroidism can be caused by:

1. Inhibition of the thyroid gland.

2. Damage of the thyroid gland due to a viral infection or auto-immune disorder.

Treatment

The effectiveness in treating an underactive thyroid gland due to a viral infection or auto-immune disorder varies.

For effective thyroid therapy place the North Pole of a magnet to the 7th cervical vertebra/back of neck and throat/thyroid area front of neck. Treatment time is thirty minutes, twice daily.

Take 6 fl ozs of Bipolar magnetised water twice daily.

NB. I do not recommend that Magnetic Therapy is a replacement for the thyroxin supplement. It can be safely used in addition to medical treatment and people suffering from such a complaint should have their blood checked as well to allow adjustments to be made by their doctor.

HYPERTHYROIDISM
(Overactivity of the Thyroid gland.)

An enlarged thyroid gland is known as goitre. There are many causes including a shortage of iodine in the diet.

Treatment

Application of the North Pole of a magnet to the 7th cervical vertebra at the back of the neck.

Also placement of the North Pole of a magnet over the enlarged gland for short periods of time.

Take 6 fl ozs of Bipolar magnetised water twice daily.

DIABETES MELLITUS

(Disorder of the carbohydrate metabolism in which sugars in the body are not oxidised to produce energy due to lack of the pancreatic hormone insulin leading to hyperglycaemia.)

Treatment

Local application of the North Pole of a magnet on pancreas for ten to fifteen minutes twice daily.

Take 4 fl ozs glass of North Pole magnetised water three times daily.

Also the North Pole of a Super Magnet may be worn on the thymus gland for one to two hours daily.

NB. It is important for people who have diabetes to keep their doctor informed as often the amount of insulin required may need adjusting.

Immune System

The immune system is a complex army of cells and antibodies which protects the body from external invaders. When the immune system is strong we are protected from many micro-organisms. If the cells of the body and immune system become overloaded with toxicity, the immune system tends to over react to the invaders.

CANCER AND THE IMMUNE SYSTEM

Anyone with a strong functioning immune system is unlikely to get a degenerative disease as the natural body's defences will be able to cope with invaders.

Cancer generally only appears when the immune system is not functioning properly or when it becomes suppressed and is unable to deal with invading toxins. Therefore, it is vital that Preventative Health Care be taken as soon as we notice that the immune system is not functioning at its optimum level. It is very important that we have a positive mental attitude to what ails us. The important issues for us to address are as listed:

1. Better nutrition.

2. Stimulation of the immune system with mineral and vitamin supplement.

3. Stress prevention and management.

4. Changes in lifestyle.

5. Most important of all is the will to live a healthy, full and creative life.

Treatment

Place the North Pole of a Super Magnet on the thymus gland. Introduce magnet gradually building up to twenty four hours for two weeks then four to six hours for four weeks.

NB. Do not use the South Pole of a magnet.

Take 6 fl ozs of North Pole magnetised water morning and evening.

The book *Fit For Life* by Harvey and Marilyn Diamond is an excellent guide for people who wish to improve their nutritional intake. It is important that we participate in monitoring our own health. We must take the primary responsibility for our health and wellbeing.

AIDS

Acquired Immune Deficiency Syndrome and AIDS-related conditions present a complicated clinical picture which generally affects the organism as a whole.

The important issues for us to address are as listed:

1. Better nutrition.

2. Stimulation of the immune system with mineral and vitamin supplement.

3. Stress prevention and management.

4. Changes in lifestyle.

5. Most important of all is the will to live a healthy, full and creative life.

NB. Do not use the South Pole of a magnet.

Treatment

The North Pole of a Super Magnet on thymus gland two to four hours daily.

Take 6 fl ozs North Pole magnetised water twice daily.

EXHAUSTION OF ADRENAL GLANDS

Adrenal glands are two endocrine glands which cover the superior surface of the kidney. Adrenaline is an important hormone secreted by the adrenal gland. It has the important function of preparing the body for *fight or flight* and has a widespread effect on circulation, muscles and sugar metabolism. The action of the heart is increased as is the rate of breathing and the metabolic rate is raised.

The main function of the adrenal glands is to maintain the body's sodium/potassium balance. If the adrenal glands are exhausted, the body may retain an excess of potassium.

SYMPTOMS ARE AS FOLLOWS:

1. Extreme fatigue in the mornings, improving as the day wears on.

2. Hypoglycaemia (low Blood Sugar).

3. Asthma.

4. Allergies.

All symptoms get worse if coffee consumption is high.

Treatment

Sleep on a magnetic bed or magnetic strip under sheet.

Apply the North Pole of a magnet to adrenal glands (kidney area) for ten to fifteen minutes daily.

Take 6 fl ozs South Pole magnetised water twice daily.

COLDS AND FLU
(Influenza.)

Treatment

Colds and flu are treated by placing the North Pole of a magnet on the chest, throat and base of brain and lymphatics, for twenty minutes three times daily.

Take 4 fl ozs of North Pole magnetised water, four to five times daily.

CHRONIC FATIGUE
(Low Energy)

- Can be caused by a viral infection
- Deficiency in the Immune System

Treatment

Sleeping on a magnetic bed or magnetic overlay is very effective.

Place the North Pole of a Super Magnet on the thymus gland for two to three hours every day to boost the immune system.

Take 6fl ozs of Bipolar magnetised water twice daily.

ME
(Myalgic Encephalonyelitis.)

ME also known as Yuppie Flu. ME is a condition that develops when the immune system has been weakened which leaves a person open to infections and viruses that come along. Candida weakens the immune system. Many people who suffer from ME have candida problems. ME presents symptoms which the body uses as a signal to the person that everything is exhausted. In the initial stages, a person does not feel well and suffers from lack of energy.

They push their bodies to keep going and in the process exhaust their adrenal glands. In its chronic stage, ME sufferers are usually so weak and ill that they can barely stand up, find it extremely difficult to concentrate and may feel dizzy.

Treatment

The body needs to be detoxified, to do this:

Take 6 fl ozs North Pole magnetised water three times daily. At a later stage when the body is detoxified Bipolar magnetised water is helpful to boost the organs and to help rejuvenate the body, take 4 fl ozs three times daily.

Place the North Pole of a Super Magnet on the thymus gland for two to four hours daily.

It is also important to treat the adrenal glands with the South Pole of a magnet for five minutes daily.

At night the North Pole of a magnet should be placed at the head of the bed.

If there is dizziness present, place the North Pole of a small magnet behind the ear. If symptoms persist change around to South Pole.

Musculoskeletal System

ARTHRITIS

Arthritis and other disorders of the musculoskeletal system comprise the most common cause of illness affecting the population. Arthritis can affect any joint in the human body.

The most common forms of arthritis are rheumatoid and osteoarthritis.

RHEUMATOID ARTHRITIS

This is the destruction of cartilage. This type of arthritis is caused by inflammation within the joint.

Treatment

Different placement of magnets can be carried out depending on the stage and location of the arthritis.

1. The North and South Pole of a magnet can be used. If the arthritis is in the upper body, place the North Pole of a magnet under the palm of the right hand and the South Pole of a magnet under the left hand for twenty to thirty minutes, two to three times daily or as required. This form of treatment usually gives relief to people suffering with arthritis of the hands.

2. If the lower body is affected, place magnets under the soles of the feet. North Pole under right foot, South Pole under left foot. As well as treating arthritis of the feet and ankles it is also beneficial for people suffering from gout and irregular or poor circulation of blood in the legs.

3. For treating left sided problems, North Pole under the palm of the left hand and South Pole under the sole of the left foot.

4. For treating right sided problems, North Pole under the right hand and South Pole under the sole of the right foot.

5. A magnetic bed can be used if available at night. If not use a large magnetic strip placed under the sheet.

6. Take 6 fl ozs Bipolar magnetised water twice daily.

7. For specific pain and inflammation apply the North Pole of a magnet to the exact location of pain and keep in position until symptoms improve.

8. South Pole magnetised oils can be massaged into painful and inflammed areas.

NB. Be careful to place magnets to the side of, above or below an encapsulated joint.

OSTEOARTHRITIS
(The result of damage or insufficiency of the cartilage on the end of the bone where it articulates or moves against another bone.)

The general symptoms are usually pain, swelling, stiffness and formation of bone spurs.

Treatment
Follow treatment for rheumatoid arthritis.

CALCIUM DEPOSITS

(Deposits of calcium can form in the blood vessels and arteries to cause clogging.)

Treatment

Place the North Pole of a magnet under right foot and South Pole under left foot for twenty minutes twice daily.

Take 6 fl ozs Bipolar water twice daily.

HEEL SPURS

(Sharp projections of calcium on the bone of the heel. Can be very painful when walking.)

Treatment

The best way is to use the North Pole of a magnet under the heel over night. Strap it on to heel and cover with a support sock to keep in position. The length of time required depends on the depth of the spur. Usually ten to fourteen days, but could take longer depending on how big the spur is and the age of the person being treated.

Take 6 fl ozs North Pole magnetised water twice daily.

STIFF OR PAINFUL NECK

Treatment

This condition responds very quickly to the application of the North Pole of a magnet over the area of stiffness or pain. Leave in place until symptoms are relieved.

Other placements of magnets can be tried as well. The application of North Pole of a Super Magnet to the 7th cervical vertebra can be effective.

CERVICAL SPONDYLITIS

(Inflammation of the Cervical Vertebrae.)

Treatment

The application of North Pole of a magnet to the affected vertebrae can be of help.

The Indian doctors Bansal and Bansal in their self help book on Magnet Therapy treat cervical spondylitis with the North Pole of a Ceramic Magnet on the affected cervical vertebrae and the South Pole on the spot where the pain extends to.

South Pole magnetised oil can be massaged into the painful area.

WHIPLASH

Caused by sudden jerking back of the head and neck. Resulting in damage to ligaments, vertebrae, spinal cord or nerve roots.

Treatment

Application of the North Pole of strong magnets to the neck and shoulder area; additional magnets can be placed on the thoracic area for thirty minutes twice a daily. Magnets may remain in position until pain subsides. Magnetic neck supports can be used. Additional magnets can be inserted, North Pole to the affected area. A magnetic pillow is highly recommended.

Magnets may be worn all day or night as required for relief of pain.

SHOULDER PAIN

Shoulder problems are often related to occupational, physical and emotional states which manifest themselves in a tightening of the trapezius muscle.

Treatment

A flexible magnetic shoulder wrap is recommended. Additional Super Magnets can be inserted on the inside of the wrap. This will give additional strength to the area. In addition a magnetic pillow can be of benefit as would a magnetic overlay.

South pole magnetised oil can be massaged into painful area.

FIBROMYALGIA

Inflammation of muscles of neck and shoulder causing pain. Fibromyalgia was previously known as Fibrositis.

Treatment

Application of the North Pole of strong magnets to the neck and shoulder area. Additional magnets can be placed on the thoracic area for thirty minutes twice daily. Magnets may remain in position until pain subsides. Magnetic neck supports can be used.

MUSCLE CRAMPS

Treatment

Muscle cramp can be treated by direct placement of the North Pole of magnets over the affected area until pain subsides.

Leg cramps can be treated by placing Ceramic Magnets on the soles of the feet - North Pole right foot, South Pole left foot for twenty minutes. Magnetic insoles may also be used.

People who suffer from leg cramps or restless legs should have a magnet at the end of the bed.

SCIATICA

Treatment

Treat the spine with a magnetic back support. Small neodymium magnets placed over the site of pain are also effective.

Usually sciatica is on one side but if both sides are affected a bilateral placement is very beneficial. Leave in place until pain is relieved. South Pole magnetised oil can be massaged into painful area.

BURSITIS

(Inflammation of the small sack of fibrous tissues which is lined with synovial membrane and filled with fluid.)

Treatment

Place the North Pole of a magnet near the area for fifteen minutes three times daily. It may be necessary to place magnets above, below or to the side of the bursitis.

NB. As bursitis happens in an encapsulated joint do not place directly on the affected area.

SKELETAL SYSTEM

There is much scientific evidence to date in the USA about how quickly injuries and broken bones are restored to health with magnetic treatment. Magnet Therapy is used a great deal in America on animals and in particular horses. It has been proven that broken bones recover in half the time if Magnet Therapy is used.

SPRAINS

Treatment

Treatment may start with RICE. Which is rest, ice, compression, and elevation. Resting for one day. Ice applied to the area three times a day. In the case of a sprained ankle, elevation can be achieved by resting it on a stool. Compression can be obtained with a magnetic flexible ankle support with the addition of extra neodinium magnets as required.

South Pole magnetised oil can be massaged into painful area.

I treat many such injuries with good results.

BROKEN BONES AND FRACTURES

Treatment

Once fracture is set and there are no metal pins involved you can commence Magnet Therapy treatment.

South Pole on the upper end of broken bone and North Pole on the lower part ensures best healing. Take 6 fl ozs North Pole magnetised water three times daily.

Nervous System

PANIC ATTACKS

Panic attacks occur when a person enters an acute state of anxiety with some or all of the following symptoms - difficulty with breathing, dizzy, sweaty, feeling faint, palpitations, nausea and fright. Duration is usually short. After it has passed the person can feel exhausted and weak.

Treatment

Apply the North Pole a magnet at the head of the bed during sleep. This placement of magnet helps raise the level of melatonin. In some cases it is beneficial to use bi-tempolar placement.

A magnetic bed used in conjunction with a magnetic pillow is recommended.

Take 4 fl ozs Bipolar magnetised water three times daily.
NB. If panic attacks become frequent, consult your physician.

DEPRESSION

Depression is likely to be helped by raising the level of melatonin.

Treatment

Whenever possible have the head of the bed facing north.

Place the North Pole of a magnet at the head of the bed nightly. In addition, bitemporal placement of the North Pole of magnets may be tried twice daily for ten to fifteen minutes.

Take 6 fl ozs Bipolar water twice daily.

ADDICTIONS

Addictions produce positive magnetic field stimulation which causes overdrive of the brain and body.

Application of North Pole magnetic energy helps to restore the state of balance.

Treatment

Place the North Pole of a magnet at the head of the bed at night. Apply the North Pole of a magnet at base of skull for five to ten minutes.

The North Pole of a magnet may be placed on right and left temples for five to ten minutes just above and in front of the ears. This has a calming effect on the system.

NB. In case of addiction medical supervision is necessary.

INSOMNIA

Anxiety and depression can be a contributing factor with insomnia.

Treatment

If possible the head of the bed should be facing North. If this is not possible the North Pole of a magnet should be placed at the head of the bed to aid a good night's sleep or apply the North Pole of a Super Magnet to the crown of the head for ten minutes before retiring.

It is also important to avoid stimulants such as coffee etc. before retiring.

Take 6 fl ozs of Bipolar magnetised water morning and evening.

MIGRAINE HEADACHES

Very often migraine headaches are caused by stress and food or chemical allergies.

Treatment

Different placements of the North Pole of a magnet should be tried near the site of the pain until symptoms subside.

A magnetic headband is a convenient appliance, extra magnets can be inserted. Neodymium magnets are recommended for severe pain.

Take 6 fl ozs Bipolar magnetised water three times daily.

HEADACHE

Treatment

Different placements of the North Pole of magnets should be tried on the head/base of skull.

Bilateral placement of magnets may be tried on the temple area. A magnetic pillow is recommended.

Take 6 fl ozs Bipolar magnetised water three times daily.

MULTIPLE SCLEROSIS

(Chronic disease of the nervous system affecting young and middle aged adults. The myelin sheaths surrounding nerves in the brain and spinal cord are damaged which affects the function of the nerves involved.)

Treatment

The South Pole of a Super Magnet placed at the base of the spine
will help to strengthen the spine allowing greater mobility. Apply for
twenty to thirty minutes twice daily. North Pole magnets can also be
applied to both legs as required.

In addition a magnetic support can be used where appropriate. Take
6 fl ozs Bipolar magnetised water, three times daily.

PARALYSIS

(Muscle weakness which varies in its extent.)

Treatment

If right side is affected apply the North Pole of a magnet under right
hand and the South Pole of a magnet under right foot for twenty
minutes twice daily.

If the condition is left-sided use opposite position - North Pole under
the palm of the left hand and South Pole under the sole of left foot
for twenty minutes twice daily.

If lower body is affected, apply the North Pole of a magnet under
right foot and the South Pole of a magnet under left foot for twenty
minutes twice daily.

TRIGEMINAL NEURALGIA

*(A sharp piercing pain which soars through the cheek or jaw and is most
common in women in their forties and fifties.)*

Treatment

The North Pole of a magnet is applied to the site of the pain. In
some cases several small magnets may be used on the area of pain
on the cheek. Japanese and American doctors have experienced
remarkable results from symptoms in such cases.

In acute cases apply a strong magnet to the face until pain subsides, but make sure that the magnet is not too near the eyes.

NB. Do not treat if there are any metals in the mouth as the magnet would adhere itself to braces

Take 4 fl ozs of North Pole magnetised water three times daily.

TOOTHACHE

Treatment

North Pole of a magnet applied directly to area of pain until symptoms are relieved. If inflammation or infection is present treatment should be continuous until doctor or dentist can be consulted.

MERCURY FILLINGS

In the case of mercury, a person could have broken a filling and if it is not sealed the mercury could be leaking into the system. Mercury is a poison and once in the system, it is difficult to remove.

Treatment

The Super Magnet is effective for removing the poison from the system. It is worn on the thymus gland which is located one inch below the V in the Neck. Usually, the North Pole of the magnet is applied for six to eight hours for about two to four weeks depending on the severity of the condition.

Reproductive System

DYSMENORRHOEA

(Painful Periods.)

Treatment

The North Pole of a magnet placed over the abdomen worn overnight for five to seven nights prior to menstruation.

Take 6 fl ozs North Pole magnetised water twice daily.

AMENORRHOEA

(Absence of Periods.)

NB. Rule out pregnancy before treatment.

Treatment

Placement of the North Pole of a magnet over abdomen overnight until condition improves. Additional placement of the North and South Poles of magnets under the feet morning and evening for twenty minutes, North Pole - right foot, South Pole - left foot.

Take 6 fl ozs of South Pole magnetised water twice daily.

INFLAMMATION OF WOMB OR OVARIES

Treatment

The North Pole of a magnet placed over womb and if ovaries are involved, placement of North Pole over each ovary. The small strong magnets are effective for this.

The placement of the North and South Poles of magnets can be used under the feet morning and evening for twenty minutes. North Pole under right foot and South Pole under left foot.

Take 6 fl ozs North Pole magnetised water twice daily.

FIBROIDS

(A benign tumour of fibrous and muscular tissue which develops in the muscular wall of the womb.)

Treatment

The North Pole of a magnet over abdomen, four to six hours daily for a period of two to three weeks.

Take 6 fl ozs North Pole magnetised water twice daily.

MENOPAUSE

Treatment

For menopausal symptoms treat uterus and ovaries.

I have found that the North Pole of a Super Magnet worn on the thymus gland for a short period of time daily - one to two hours - has a very balancing affect on the body. It helps ward off mood swings, depression and is also effective with general aches and pains.

Take 6 fl ozs South Pole magnetised water three times daily.

OVARIAN CYSTS

Treatment

Direct application of the North Pole of a Super Magnet over the area. Wear overnight in bed.

PRE-MENSTRUAL SYNDROME
(PMS.)
Treatment

The North Pole of a magnet at the crown of the head and the base of the neck and bilateral placement on temporal area.

Different placements on the head can be tried until relief is achieved.

Magnetic strip can also be placed in the bed under the sheet.

In addition oil of evening primrose capsules and vitamin B6 can be taken daily.

Take 6 fl ozs Bipolar magnetised water twice daily.

OSTEOPOROSIS

(Decreased bone density, it is a natural process of ageing.)

Treatment

The North Pole of a magnet placed on the 7th cervical vertebra for thirty minutes twice daily.
Sleeping on a magnetic bed or magnetic overlay is very effective.
Take 6 fl ozs Bipolar magnetised water daily.
A diet rich in calcium or a calcium supplement is advisable.

ENDOMETRIOSIS

The endometrium is the mucous membrane lining the uterus. Inflammation of the endometrium is known as endometriosis. The condition is usually restricted to the neck of the womb but may also affect the ovaries and the fallopian tubes. It is an extremely painful condition.

Treatment

Place the North Pole of the super magnet on the abdomen nightly for four to six weeks. Take 6fl ozs North Pole water twice daily.

PROSTATE PROBLEMS
(Enlarged prostate gland)

The prostate gland is situated just below the bladder. The prostate surrounds the Urethra, the tube, which takes urine from the bladder. If the prostate becomes enlarged it may constrict the urethra, preventing the normal flow of urine, causing retention of urine and pain in the lower abdomen.

Treatment

The North Pole of a magnet should be applied directly to the area for one to two hours daily. The North Pole of a magnet may also be applied to groin area for twenty minutes twice daily.

Take 6 fl ozs South Pole magnetised water twice daily.

ORCHIDITIS

(Inflammation of the testis which causes pain, redness and swelling of the scrotum.)

Treatment

Place the North Pole of a magnet to the affected area for one to two hours daily.

Take 6 fl ozs North Pole magnetised water twice daily.

Respiratory System

CHEST PROBLEMS

BRONCHITIS

(Inflammation of the bronchi is caused by a virus or bacteria.)

Treatment

Initial application of the North Pole of a magnet for half an hour three times daily on thymus gland. The time can be increased by degrees up to two hours.

If a person has chronic bronchitis it is possible that they can go into a bronchospasm. If this happens remove the magnet and re-introduce it at a later stage.

Take 6 fl ozs North Pole magnetised water twice daily.

ASTHMA

(Condition characterised by paroxysmal attacks of bronchospasm causing difficulty in breathing.)

Treatment

Follow same treatment as bronchitis.

EMPHYSEMA

(Air in the tissues of the lungs.)

Treatment

Follow same treatment as bronchitis.

SINUSITIS

(Inflammation of the membrane lining the facial sinuses.)

Sinusitis is often caused by infection spreading from the nose. Symptoms can include stuffy nose, headache, tenderness over the affected sinus, post-nasal drip.

Treatment

Various placements of North Pole magnets can be tried. North Pole magnets should be placed to the side or below the sinuses to draw mucus out of the area.

The North Pole of a magnet can also be applied to the forehead. The small strong magnets can be placed on either side of the nose - North Pole on the right side and South Pole on the left side for ten to fifteen minutes twice daily.

Take 6fl ozs of North Pole magnetised water three times daily.

With sinusitis food allergies should be considered.

SORE THROAT

Treatment

Place the North Pole of a Super Magnet on the throat until inflammation subsides.

An additional magnet can be placed on the 7th cervical vertebra area.

The placement of magnets to side of neck can be beneficial and especially useful for people suffering from tonsillitis.

Take 6 fl ozs of North Pole magnetised water four times daily.

Gargle using North Pole magnetised water.

Once pain and inflammation have subsided the South Pole of a magnet can be applied to strengthen the throat for ten minutes daily.

Skin

ACNE

(Skin disorder in which sebaceous glands become inflamed.)

Treatment

The North Pole of a magnet is applied directly to the area for twenty minutes twice daily.

Bathe the skin with North Pole magnetised water.

Take 6 fl ozs North Pole magnetised water morning and evening.

Often acne is caused by food allergies, especially to dairy and sugar products. If allergy is suspected an allergy test is advised.

ECZEMA

(Superficial inflammation of the skin with a red and itchy rash, sometimes with blisters that become crusted.)

Treatment

The North and South Poles of magnets under hands and feet. North Pole under right hand and right foot, South Pole under the left hand and left foot, fifteen to twenty minutes twice daily.

Take 6 fl ozs North Pole magnetised water twice daily.

NB. Food and stress are contributing factors.

PSORIASIS

(Itchy scaly red patches form on the skin mainly elbows, forearms, knees, legs and scalp.)

Treatment

Treat as instructed for eczema.

DERMATITIS

(Inflammation of the skin usually caused by outside agents - mainly cleaning and washing agents.)

Treatment

Treat as instructed for eczema.

RING WORM

(Fungus infection of the surface of the skin which is highly contagious. It forms rings and is intensely itchy.)

Treatment

The North Pole of a magnet on ring worm spot. Leave in position for several days.

Take 6 fl ozs North Pole magnetised water twice daily.

MINOR BURNS

Treatment

Initially apply some ice to the area. After about five minutes apply the North Pole of a magnet to the affected area until the pain and inflammation subsides.

A small strong magnet is the best for small burns. However, if it is a larger burn then a larger magnet would be more appropriate because it would cover a greater area. The use of the magnetic strip can be effective.

NB. Do not use the South Pole (positive magnetic energy) with an open wound or when infection is present. The South Pole of a magnet is used to strengthen and to enhance and should be used sparingly.

SCAR TISSUE

Magnet Therapy is very effective for treating a wound or scar tissue post-operatively.

Treatment

With the application of the North Pole of a magnet the scar will reduce in size very quickly. It is best to treat with North Pole of magnets or a magnetic strip overnight.

SHINGLES

(Inflammation of the skin caused by a virus and characterised by collections of small blisters.)

Treatment

Direct application of the North Pole a magnet to the area for fifteen minutes three times daily.

If eyes are affected low strength North Poles of magnets may be applied for five minutes twice daily.

Take 6 fl ozs North Pole magnetised water.

Bathe area with North Pole magnetised water.

NB. It is advisable to boil and cool water before magnetising.

BITES/STINGS

Treatment

The North Pole of a magnet over the affected area until symptoms are relieved.

Take 6 fl ozs North Pole magnetised water.

WARTS

Treatment

Strong magnets are most effective in the treatment of warts.

Use a small strong North Pole magnet over the area for five to seven days.

If there are several warts use North Pole magnetised water to bathe the warts several times daily.

Take 6 fl ozs North Pole magnetised water three times daily.

CHILDREN'S WARTS

Treatment

Bathe warts three times daily in magnetised water.

Apply the North Pole of a magnet for shorter periods.

A small strong magnet may be strapped over wart.

Give 2 fl ozs North Pole magnetised water three times daily.

MOLES

Treatment

Place the North Pole of a magnet over the area and strap to keep it in position. A small magnet is best and should be left in position for at least five to seven days.

Special Senses

EAR PROBLEMS - DIZZINESS, VERTIGO

Treatment

The North Pole of a small magnet placed behind the ear until symptoms are relieved.

If symptoms do not improve, place small pieces of magnetic strips behind the ears. This can be very effective because it has the strength of both North and South Poles.

Sometimes dizziness can be caused by other conditions such as hypertension or food allergies.

EAR ACHE

Treatment

Place the North Pole of a small magnet behind or in front of ear. Leave in position until symptoms are relieved If symptoms are not relieved try different placements.

Also treat neck - 7th cervical vertebra by applying the North Pole of a magnet until symptoms are relieved.

TINNITUS

(Ringing in the ears.)

Tinnitus can be caused by food allergies. Wheat is often suspect in such cases.

Another contributing factor can be metal fillings in the teeth setting up an electrical current in the mouth which causes a disturbance within the energy system as well as ringing in the ears.

Treatment

A small Super Magnet is usually very beneficial in this area. Placement of the North Pole of a magnet behind ears until symptoms are relieved.

NB. If ringing in the ears disappears when magnets are applied and reappears when they are removed contact your doctor or dentist regarding the possibility of electrical interference from metal fillings in the teeth.

CATARACTS

(Cataracts are caused by lack of sufficient oxygen to the eyes.)

Treatment

The North Pole of a low strength magnet applied over the eyelid for five minutes minutes twice daily.

GLAUCOMA

*(Condition caused when the fluid in the eye is so abnormally high
that it causes damage.)*

NB. In such cases magnets should not be placed directly over the eye as it will draw fluid into the eye and increase pressure (as it is an encapsulated joint).

Treatment

Apply the North Pole of a magnet to the side and below the eye to draw fluid away from the eye for five minutes, three times daily.

CONJUNCTIVITIS

(Inflammation of the conjunctiva of the eyes producing redness, swelling, watery or puss discharge.)

Treatment

Use North Pole magnetised water to wash the eyes. Use North Pole magnetised water as eye drops four times daily.

NB. It is advisable to boil and cool water before magnetising.

Urinary System

KIDNEY PROBLEMS

(General.)

Treatment

Treat kidneys with bilateral placement of North Pole of a magnet ten to fifteen minutes twice daily.

The placement of a magnetic strip down the spine and the South Pole of a magnet in the lumbar region is usually effective. Apply for twenty minutes twice daily.

Take 6 fl ozs Bipolar magnetised water three times daily before meals.

RENAL CALCULI

(Kidney Stones.)

Spasomidic severe pain radiating down the groin and inner sides of thighs caused by a stone in either kidney.

Treatment

The North Pole of a strong magnet should be applied to painful area over kidneys or abdomen and left in position until pain has subsided.

In addition magnets can also be placed under feet morning and evening for thirty minutes - North Pole right foot and South Pole left foot.

Take 6 fl ozs North Pole magnetised water four times daily.

CYSTITIS

(Inflammation of the urinary tract often caused by infection.)

Treatment

Use direct application of North Pole magnets to the kidneys, ureters and bladder for one to three hours daily until symptoms subside.

Take 6 fl ozs North Pole magnetised water three times daily.

Magnet Therapy - A Holistic Approach

PREVENTATIVE HEALTH

In this present day there is much emphasis placed on Preventative Care. In essence what Preventative Care really means is taking responsibility for our own wellbeing.

Speaking personally, having used magnets for many years, I have found them to be a great aid to keeping the body, mind and spirit well balanced. Magnet Therapy is safe, non-intrusive and very effective.

However, as I have said on many occasions in this book, we must look after our lives - physically, mentally, emotionally and spiritually. None of us are immune from illness. When it does hit us we should treat it as a lesson to see how out of step we are in our lives.

Magnet Therapy on its own does not heal, it facilities the body to enable it to heal itself.

Magnet Therapy and Complementary Medicine

HOMEOPATHY

The founder of homeopathy, Dr Samuel Hahnemann (1755-1843), conducted many experiments using Magnet Therapy over a long period of time. When he was fully convinced about the beneficial effects of magnetism he wrote strongly in its favour.

Dr Hahnemann wrote extensively about medicines prepared from magnets. In his works he gave detailed information about magnets, including the method of preparation, describing the symptoms covered by the medicines prepared from three different properties of magnets. So we can see from this how Magnet Therapy is closely allied to homeopathy.

ACUPUNCTURE/ACUPRESSURE

Many acupuncturists now use Magnet Therapy in conjunction with their acupuncture and the same is true of therapists who practice acupressure.

Finally

It is not intended that Magnet Therapy be a substitute for medicine. Magnet Therapy like many other Complementary Therapies is an aid to orthodox medicine. We still need to visit our general practitioner or consultant when necessary.
One should never discontinue or readjust medication without medical supervision.

I have tried to give as much information as possible in this book. However, there is always so much more to learn especially with ongoing research. The contents of this book are mainly drawn from my own experience, plus extensive research in Magnet Therapy.

I am particularly grateful to the pioneers in the area of Magnet Therapy. The original books written by such people as Albert Roy Davis, Doctors Bansal and Bansal, Dr Santwani, Dr Bangali and many other enlightened people have provided a strong foundation for the progress and future of Magnet Therapy in the prevention and treatment of illness.

I would also like to express my sincere thanks to all my teachers who have helped and guided me throughout the years and also to the people whose books were a great source of inspiration to me.
To my friends who are too numerous to mention for their wonderful confidence in me. Finally, to the readers of this book, while I have imparted as much knowledge as I could to you, the best way forward is to become familiar with your magnet. Experiment with it for yourself and treat it with respect. We use the magnet as a tool, never forgetting that we too must play our part in keeping ourselves healthy and also to encourage those with whom we work to do the same.

Reference Books

1 *Magneto Therapy* - Self Help Book
   Dr H L Bansal & Dr R S Bansal

2 *Magnetic Cure for Common Diseases*
   Dr H L Bansal & Dr R S Bansal

3 *Magneto Therapy for Common Diseases*
   Dr M T Santwani

4 *Magnet Therapy Theory and Practice*
   Dr Neville S Bengali

5 *Discovery of Magnetic Health*
   George J Washnis and Richard Z Hricak

6 *Biomagnetic Hand Book*
   William H Pphilpott M D and Sharon Taplin

7 *Magnet Therapy and Balancing your Body's Energy*
   Flow for Self-Healing
   Holga Hannemann

INDEX OF TREATMENTS

Consultations, Magnet Therapy treatments, training,
allergy testing, and magnets are available
by contacting Rosemary Skinner
at Phone/Fax: (Ireland) 00353-1-2884925
email: rosemaryskinner@ireland.com

Recommended suppliers of quality magnetic products:

Magnetic Therapy Ltd.
Walkden
Worsley
Manchester M28 9DU
England
Phone: 0845 1305110
Fax: 0845 1305055